UP HERE, FEAR'S NOT AN OPTION.

YOU CAN FALL SIXTY STORIES OR SLIP IN THE SHOWER.

DIE TRYING

CHUCK DIXON...... WRITER
SCOTT McDANIEL... PENCILLER
KARL STORY...... INKER
ROBERTA TEWES.... COLORIST
JOHN COSTANZA.... LETTERER
DARREN VINCENZO.. ASSOCIATE EDITOR
SCOTT PETERSON... EDITOR

WORRYING ABOUT IT'S A WASTE OF TIME.

MUST BE A DESPERATE CREW.

TANGLEWOOD'S ONE OF THOSE FAILED URBAN MALLS.

HALF THE STORES ARE CLOSED.

THE REST SELL LOW-END MERCHANDISE.

CLOTHING KNOCK-OFFS. COSTUME JEWELRY. OFF-BRAND STEREOS.

LUCKY FOR ME THE FOOD COURT DOESN'T GET LOCKED UP.

GREASE.

UK.

IF I CAN'T JUST PUT SOME DISTANCE BETWEEN ME AND THEIR GUNS I CAN WORK MY WAY AROUND THEM TO--

MAN...

ONE HOT ROUND INTO A PROPANE TANK AND--

THESE GUYS ARE TOO WELL ARMED FOR RETAIL BURGLARY.

AND SOME BURGLARY.

THE WHOLE MALL LIT UP LIKE CHRISTMAS.

A GULF-WAR LEVEL FIREFIGHT.

AND NOT A COP IN SIGHT.

YOUR BREAKFAST IS ON THE TABLE. I'M ON *OPENINGS* AT O'SHAUGHNESSY'S ALL WEEK AND I'VE *GOT* TO JET.

CAN YOU GET THE KIDS OFF TO SCHOOL?

WHY NOT?

DONNA...

WHAT?

WHY'S IT SO HARD FOR ME AND *BRUCE* MAKES IT LOOK SO EASY?

I REALLY *CAN'T* GO INTO IT, HONEY--

MAYBE BECAUSE YOU'RE *YOU* AND HE'S *HIM.*

I DUNNO.

JUST MAKE SURE SKIP TAKES HIS RIDALYN!

OH--

--KAY.

HEY! DAD!

HUH?

DIDJA SEE MR. WAYNE'S NEW CAR?

IT'S SO *COOL!*

VIDLINK....

GRAYSON!

UBBA-UBBA-BUH-

YES, MR. KERR?

THIS IS JEAN PAUL VALLEY. HE'S NEW TO YOUR DEPARTMENT.

SHOW HIM THE ROPES.

SHUH-SURE THING.

AND WHAT POSITION IS VALLEY FILLING, SIR?

UNIT SUPERVISOR! HE'S YOUR NEW IMMEDIATE SUPERIOR! BRUCE WAYNE'S MOVING UP TO VICE PRESIDENT OF OPERATIONS.

OH.

AND THAT'S MISTER VALLEY, GRAYSON.

CKETY-CLACK
CLA
WE CAN ELIMINATE BELONEPHOBIA AND DEIPNOPHOBIA.
IT'S SOMETHING MORE *PROFOUND* THAN THAT.
NOT SOMETHING THAT *REPELS* YOU.
A FEAR THAT DRIVES YOU.
L-CLACKETY-CLA
CKET
WHAT ARE YOU AFRAID OF?
AFRAID OF?

I KNOW SOAMES IS DIRTY.

BUT I DON'T HAVE ANYTHING ON HIM EXCEPT WHAT I'VE SEEN.

AND THE LAW IN BLÜDHAVEN ISN'T GOING TO HELP.

THEY'D SHOOT ME AND PIN A MEDAL ON HIM.

HAVE TO MONITOR HIS MOVES.

EVEN AS COOL AS HE IS, SOAMES HAS TO MAKE A MISTAKE.

I THINK I CAN PUSH HIM TOWARD IT.

LATER.

I'M NOT EXACTLY A MORNING PERSON.

50

YOU'RE NOT LEAVING ME HERE, SOAMES.

I CAN'T SEE WHY *NOT*, CRANE.

BUT AFTER ALL I'VE *DONE* FOR YOU AND BLOCK-BUSTER--!

HA!

NIGHTWING MAY HAVE ESCAPED BUT HE'S NOT THE MAN HE *WAS*.

THE PSYCHOACTIVE DRUGS I'VE ADMINISTERED TO HIM ARE *STILL* IN HIS SYSTEM.

HE'LL BE DISORIENTED. EXPERIENCING EPISODES.

EPISODES?

FLASHBACKS TO THE *DELUSIONS* CREATED BY HIS DEEPEST FEARS AND PARANOIAS.

GIVE ME A *BIT* OF AN EDGE THEN.

FOR *THAT* I'LL LEAVE THE TELEVISION ON FOR YOU. I'LL BE BACK LATER.

SOAMES!

FEEL WEIRD.

EDGY.

SEEING THINGS AT THE CORNERS OF MY VISION.

EIGHT HOURS SOUND SLEEP SHOULD FIX THAT.

DICK?

ARE Y'HOME?

CLANCY. MY SUPER.

IF I'M NICE AND QUIET SHE'LL--

IT'LL ONLY TAKE A MINUTE, DICK.

WAY TO GO, NINJA MASTER.

I NEED THAT SLEEP.

OOP!

JUST A--UH-- SECOND!

DON'T MEAN T'BE A BOTHER.

NO--UM-- BOTHER!

BED NOT SLEPT IN.

AND THERE'S NO EXPLAINING THESE PAJAMAS.

JEEZE! Y'SCARED THE DEVIL FROM ME!

I--I--I THOUGHT--

OOH.

YER WRINGIN' WITH SWEAT. IT'S A FEVER, I THINK.

MAN, I DON'T FEEL SO GOOD.

YOU LIE BACK NOW. GET SOME SLEEP. I'LL CHECK ON YOU LATER.

THANKS, CLANCY. YOU DON'T REALLY HAVE TO.

I AIN'T NO SISTER OF MERCY, BOYO. I'M THE LANDLADY.

AND TENANTS THAT PAY THEIR RENT ON TIME ARE WORTH KEEPIN' ALIVE.

HAS TO BE A RESIDUAL EFFECT OF THE SCARECROW'S POTIONS

HOPE I CAN SLEEP IT OFF.

I'VE GOT WORK TO DO TONIGHT.

THERE'S SOME MISTAKE HERE, LADDIES--

I WAS EXPECTIN' MR. DESMOND.

NO MISTAKE, INSPECTOR.

MR. DESMOND'S PREOCCUPIED WITH OTHER PROBLEMS.

SO, I'M A "PROBLEM" NOW.

THE GREAT "DEADLY" SOAMES.

YOU BEEN WALKING A RAZOR FOR *YEARS*, SOAMES.

YOU BEEN *HEADIN'* FOR A SLIP.

LOOKS LIKE *TODAY'S* THE DAY.

IS IT NOW?

FREEZE!

NOBODY HERE BUT STRAWBOY.

WHERE'S SOAMES? WE GOT A WARRANT ON HIM.

DOES IT *LOOK* LIKE I'M IN HIS CONFIDENCE, YOU IDIOTS?

START THINKING OF WAYS TO BE *HELPFUL*, HAYSEED.

WE'RE TOSSING AWAY OUR MIRANDA CARDS HERE. CAPISH?

CRANE'S GOING TO TAKE THE LONG WAY BACK TO ARKHAM.

REDHORN MIGHT EVENTUALLY REGRET DEALING WITH SCARECROW THAT WAY, THOUGH.

NOW TO FIND SOAMES.

61

BUT TO THREATEN ME *HERE.*

I AM SORRY FOR THIS DISTURBANCE, MOTHER. THIS MAN IS A *FORMER* ASSOCIATE.

HE IS SOON TO *RETIRE.*

IS THAT WHAT Y'*CALL* IT, ROLLY?

IS THAT MY *REWARD*? A BULLET IN THE HEAD AND AN UNMARKED GRAVE?

HAS THIS NIGHTWING CHARACTER GOT YOU THAT *SPOOKED*? I THOUGHT YOU'D *COVER* ME, GET ME OUT OF THE 'HAVEN.

I FEARED THE INTEREST OF *THE BATMAN.* AS IT TURNS OUT, THIS NIGHTWING IS *JUST* AS DANGEROUS.

HE'S STRUCK AT THE VERY *FOUNDATIONS* OF MY OPERATIONS IN BLÜDHAVEN, SOMETHING I WOULD NOT HAVE THOUGHT POSSIBLE.

BUT HE CAN ONLY TIE ME TO ILLEGALITIES THROUGH *YOU.* A LIVING, *BREATHING* YOU.

TELL THIS MAN TO *LEAVE,* ROLLY.

I'LL BE *LEAVIN',* MOTHER DESMOND.

AFTER I'VE MADE THINGS RIGHT WITH YOUR *SAINTED* SON.

ESPECIALLY WHEN I KNOW WHAT'S GOING TO HAPPEN WHEN I LEAVE THE ROOM.

ROLLY!

SOAMES' BIG MAGNUM FIRES FOUR TIMES.

IT'S CUT OFF BY A ROAR THAT SHAKES THE FLOOR AND RATTLES THE WINDOWS.

RRRRRRRRR

TRIED TO MAKE LIKE A HARDENED THUG.

LOOK AT HIM. HE'S JUST A KID.

A STREETWISE KID.

COULD BE USEFUL. WITH SOAMES DEAD I HAVE NO INFORMANTS.

I NEVER THOUGHT ABOUT A SIDEKICK.

NEVER THOUGHT ABOUT HAVING MY OWN "ROBIN."

AND I GUESS IT'S BETTER I DON'T.

OOP!

NOT THAT HE WAS EVER RELIABLE.

ACROSS SCRIMSHAW PARK TOWARD WOOLRICH AVENUE.

YOU GONNA LIVE ON OUR BLOCK, YOU GOTTA PAY *RENT*, MUTT.

I ALMOST GOT *CAUGHT* T'NIGHT! I DINNIT GET NUFFIN!

NUTHIN' HERE, DIBS.

THIS IS *NUTS*.

I CAN HEAR THEM BUT CAN'T *FIND* THEM.

YOU KNOW YOUR *PROBLEM*, MUTT?

YOU DON'T *BELONG* NOWHERE.

YOU CAN'T EVEN LIVE IN THIS *DUMP* 'LESS WE SAY SO.

UNNH!

YOU AIN'T WHITE. YOU AIN'T BLACK. YOU AIN'T LATINO. YOU AIN'T ASIAN.

YOU AIN'T *NUTHIN'*.

EVEN YOUR OWN *MAMA* DIDN'T WANT YOU.

SO THEN MY MOTHER COMES OVER WITH A CASSEROLE DISH--

AND *THAT'S* WHEN IT HIT THE FAN?

YOU GOT A TIRE FIRE OVER ON SCRIMSHAW OFF MELVILLE PARK.

THIS KID'S SWALLOWED A LOT OF SMOKE AND HAS A HEAD INJURY.

RUN HIM OVER TO ST BERNIE'S, AND HURRY.

WULP!

KAF! KAF!

GOT TO DO SOMETHING ABOUT A CAR.

JUST ENOUGH TIME TO SHOWER OFF THE RUBBER STINK AND GET TO HOGAN'S.

SOMETHIN' ON YOUR MIND, KID?

YEAH. MAYBE YOU CAN HELP.

HEY, PAL. CAN YOU STAND A VISITOR?

FRANKIE DEEVER'S BACHELOR PARTY.

HIS DAD IS "LUNCH-MEAT" DEEVER, A SPECIALIST IN MURDER FOR MONEY.

YEARS IN GOTHAM GAVE ME A SIXTH SENSE FOR DANGER.

IN THIS TOWN YOU NEED SENSES SEVEN THROUGH NINE.

AND YOU DON'T GET YEARS TO DEVELOP THEM.

DOWN AND ROLL!

IF I KNEW WHERE FRANKIE'S BACHELOR BASH WAS--

--THEN SOMEONE ELSE COULD TOO.

ALL PART OF BLÜDHAVEN'S YEAR-ROUND GANG WAR.

AGHK!

OOH!

PARANOIA'S A WAY OF LIFE AROUND HERE.

ANY IDEAS?

POSSIBLY EDDIE MINH'S OUTFIT. MINH'S NOT UNDER BLOCK-BUSTER'S THUMB YET.

YET.

YOU SAY YOU HAVEN'T ANY HARD EVIDENCE TO TIE DESMOND TO ANY OF THE CRIMES COMMITTED ON HIS ORDERS?
WITH DUDLEY SOAMES DEAD THERE'S NO CONNECTION TO BLOCKBUSTER.
THE BRIDEGROOM IS THE KEY?
HIS FATHER IS TIMOTHY DEEVER A.K.A. "LUNCHMEAT."
DADDY'S BUSINESS IS "REMOVALS." GO AGAINST HIM AND YOU WIND UP IN SIX DIFFERENT TRASHBAGS.
HE CAN BE TIED TO BLOCKBUSTER?
ANGEL MARIN AND HIS TWENTY-ONE PALS WERE ROLAND DESMOND'S LAST "PUBLIC" DISPLAY OF HIS POWER.
HE'S USING DEEVER TO CLEAN UP HIS MISTAKES NOW.
YOU KNOW, YOU HAVE TO DO SOME-THING ABOUT A CAR.

BUT IF HE COULD BE TAKEN TO DREXEL'S FACILITY IN AVALON HEIGHTS--

--HE'D HAVE A FIGHTING CHANCE TO COME BACK FROM THIS TRAGEDY.

AND DREXEL WOULD PAY ALL THE BILLS.

BUT SOAMES HAS NO FAMILY EXCEPT THE POLICE FORCE.

NO ONE TO *RELEASE* HIM FROM THE HOSPITAL'S CARE.

THERE *HAS* TO BE A WAY.

ONLY ONE. AND IT'S NOT EXACTLY *KOSHER*.

WE COULD "*JOHN DOE*" HIM.

WHATEVER IT *TAKES*, DR. STROUD.

DEET DEET DEET DEET

YOU WILL *PRAY FOR DEATH*.

YES.

YOU OPENED YOUR *STITCHES,* DIDN'T YOU, ROLLY?

I'LL BE ALL RIGHT, MOTHER.

IS IT THAT *HORRIBLE* YOUNG MAN AGAIN? THAT MASKED HOOLIGAN?

WORSE, MOTHER.

NIGHTWING IS BOTHERSOME ENOUGH.

BUT HIS *MENTOR* IS IN BLÜDHAVEN NOW, UNLESS THEY'RE STOPPED THEY'LL MAKE NO END OF TROUBLE FOR ME.

WELL, I KNOW WHAT ALWAYS CHEERED YOU UP *BEFORE,* ROLLY.

REALLY, MOTHER.

I DON'T SEE HOW *HOT COCOA* IS GOING TO AMELIORATE THIS SITUATION.

THAT'S BECAUSE YOU'RE NOT A *MOTHER,* ROLLY DEAR.

105

SO WHAT ARE YOU DOING FOR A LAIR?

YOU'RE LOOKING AT IT.

YOU'RE WORKING OUT OF AN APARTMENT?

I DON'T HAVE YOUR DEEP POCKETS FOR A CAVE AND CARS AND ALL THE OTHER COOL STUFF.

YOU HAVE RESOURCES, DICK.

I OWN A TRAVELING BIG TENT CIRCUS--

I'M LUCKY IF IT BREAKS EVEN.

AND I'M NOT ABOUT TO TAP THE WAYNE FORTUNE, IF THAT'S WHAT YOU MEAN.

THERE IS YOUR TRUST FUND.

HUH?

YOUR PARENTS HAD SOME MONEY SET ASIDE FOR YOU. THEY COULD NEVER GET INSURANCE IN THEIR LINE OF WORK.

I HAD LUCIUS FOX LOOK AFTER IT WHEN I TOOK YOU IN.

WHUH-WHUH-WHAT KIND OF MONEY ARE WE TALKING ABOUT?

I DON'T HAVE AN EXACT FIGURE.

BUT YOU KNOW LUCIUS' SKILL IN THE MARKETS.

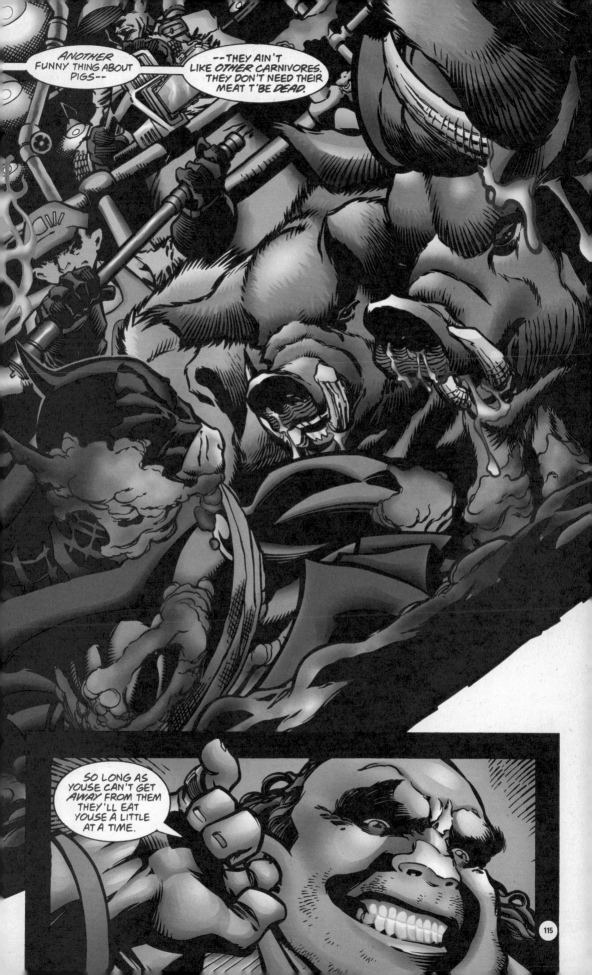

AND I GUESS I'M SUPPOSED TO JUST HIDE IN MY ROOM?

IT WON'T BE NECESSARY FOR YOU TO ENTERTAIN.

HM!

DON'T BE LIKE THAT, MOTHER.

I'LL BE LIKE ANYTHING I PLEASE, ROLLY.

THAT WILL BE ALL, SAMUEL.

AS YOU WISH, MR. DESMOND.

CHAMPAGNE? FRENCH, I HOPE.

NONE OF THAT GHASTLY NEW ZEALAND SWILL.

A '71 BRUT FROM MY PRIVATE STOCK. A PARTICULARLY GOOD SEASON IN AVIGNON.

NOTHING BUT THE FINEST FOR YOU--

--LADY VIC.

I SEE THREE GLASSES. I'M SURE YOU KNOW THAT I PREFER TO WORK ALONE.

THIS IS A SPECIAL CASE, M'LADY. IT WILL REQUIRE YOU TO WORK WITH ANOTHER.

129

AND I'M ON ANY TEAM *YOU'RE* A PART OF, HONEY.

AND WHAT ARE *YOU* CALLED?

NAME'S *STALLION.*

REFER TO ME AS "HONEY" ONCE MORE AND YOU WILL MORE ACCURATELY BE CALLED "GELDING."

NONE OF THAT FRENCH TUBWATER FOR *ME,* MR. DESMOND. I LIKE MY BUBBLY *MILWAUKEE* BREWED.

AND ITS BOUQUET MATCHES YOUR *OWN.*

YOU DON'T *NEED* TO TRY SO HARD, BABE.

SAVE YOUR ANIMUS FOR THE ENEMY.

AND WHO IS THIS QUARRY THIS TIME?

IT WILL BE A REMATCH FOR YOU AND NIGHTWING, M'LADY.

AND THE *BATMAN* MAY WELL BE ACCOMPANYING HIM.

I'LL DRINK TO *THAT!*

IT'S A TANGLED WEB, ALL RIGHT, DICK.

BUT A PATTERN EMERGES.

RUN IT DOWN FOR ME, BARBARA.

I RAN A *VENN DIAGRAM*. THAT'S WHAT YOU'RE LOOKING AT NOW.

EACH OF THOSE CIRCLES REPRESENTS A LEGITIMATE BUSINESS THE DEEVER CLAN HAS AN INTEREST IN--

--AND THOSE THEY HAVE A *RELATIONSHIP* WITH.

WHO OWNS THE OTHER CIRCLES?

SOME ARE STRICTLY LEGIT.

THE REST BELONG TO ROLAND DESMOND.

SO THEY CAN BE TIED TOGETHER UNDER THE RICO LAWS.

WHICH MAKES IT THE *FEDERAL CASE* YOU WERE LOOKING FOR.

SURE.

YOU DON'T SOUND TOO *EXCITED* ABOUT THIS, DICK.

IT'S NOT THIS, BABS. IT'S SOMETHING ELSE.

CAN WE TALK ABOUT IT ANOTHER TIME?

NO PROBLEM-- YOU KNOW WHERE TO FIND ME. ORACLE OUT.

AW... I REALLY NEEDED TO TALK TO HIM IN PERSON.

A PROBLEM, SIR?

WELL... I GUESS I HAD A CHIP ON MY SHOULDER WHEN HE WAS HERE.

YOU SURPRISE ME, SIR.

OKAY, I DESERVED THAT, ALFRED.

EVER SINCE HE CHOSE JEAN PAUL OVER ME TO FILL IN AS BATMAN I'VE BEEN A LITTLE SENSITIVE.

I'M SO BUSY MAKING MY OWN WAY I'M FORGETTING WHO SET ME ON THE PATH.

BUT IT'S NOT LIKE HE MAKES ANY OF THIS EASY. HE'S ALWAYS SO COLD, EVEN WITH ME.

EVEN AFTER EVERYTHING WE'VE BEEN THROUGH...

WHY CAN'T WE CONNECT? WHY ARE WE ALWAYS LIKE THIS?

AND... I THINK I SAID SOME THINGS TO HIM THAT WERE MEANT TO HURT.

MASTER BRUCE WOULD PROBABLY APPRECIATE HEARING THIS FROM YOURSELF.

YEAH.

I SHALL TELL HIM YOU CALLED.

THANKS.

I TAGGED ALONG.

AND I FOUGHT ALL THE HARDER BECAUSE OF IT.

HE WAS THE ONLY ONE WHO ACKNOWLEDGED ME.

SOMETIMES THAT ONLY MADE IT WORSE.

GREAT WORK, ROBIN.

140

GOOD WORK, PARTNER.

IN GOTHAM THAT FEW SECONDS OF TAPE WOULD BE ENOUGH.

GORDON COULD USE IT TO GET AN INVESTIGATION GOING.

BUT IN BLÜDHAVEN THE CORRUPTION BEGINS IN THE MAYOR'S OFFICE AND TRICKLES DOWN.

WE'RE GOING TO HAVE TO GET DEEVER HIMSELF TO TURN.

NOT A WORD 'BOUT THAT JUROR WE TOOK OUT FOR 'IM.

JEEZE...

THAT'S *NUTHIN'!* YOU CAN'T BUILD A CASE OFFA *THAT!*

IT'S A ILLEGAL TAP! IT'S NOT WORTH *SQUAT!*

WILL *BLOCKBUSTER* AGREE WITH THAT?

WOOO...

BUH... BUH... BUH...

RED ROSE

ROLAND DESMOND'S PLACE IS OVER IN AVALON HILL.

WITH AN UNOBSTRUCTED VIEW OF THE CITY HE OWNS.

BLOCKBUSTER'S BOUGHT THE BEST GUNS MONEY CAN BUY.

IT'S S.R.O. IN THE WOODS AND DUNES AROUND THE BIG HOUSE.

A TEN-ACRE FIREBASE ON THE SHORES OF GOTHAM BAY.

THE BIG GUY'S WORRIED.

HE KNOWS WE'RE COMING.

THE LAST TIME I WAS HERE SECURITY WAS TEN PERCENT OF THIS.

AND IT WILL ONLY GET TIGHTER INSIDE.

IF YOU MAKE IT THAT FAR, GUYS.

WE DON'T *HAVE* TO DANCE THIS DANCE AGAIN, DESMOND.

YOU EXPECT ME TO GO *MEEKLY*, HERO?

WE GOT LUNCHMEAT DEEVER AND HIS SON OUT OF BLÜDHAVEN.

THEY TURNED THEMSELVES IN TO U.S. MARSHALS IN GOTHAM.

THEY'RE IN *WITNESS PROTECTION,* BLOCKBUSTER.

THEY CAN TIE YOU TO *HOW MANY* MURDERS?

YOU *HAVEN'T WON,* HERO.

I CAN FIND DEEVER WITH A *SINGLE PHONE CALL.*

A CALL I'LL MAKE ONCE I'VE DISPOSED OF *YOU.*

I LEARNED MY LESSON LAST TIME WE TANGLED.

DON'T THINK SO.

I FEEL A TREMOR.

AND IT'S NOT ALL DESMOND.

ARRR!

NO TIME TO GET CLEAR.

EH?

THE CONCRETE SWALE IS MY ONLY CHANCE.

AND IT'S A SLIM ONE.

OH NO...

THE SOUND FLATTENS ME TO THE GROUND.

AS THE WHOLE WORLD SLIDES BY ABOVE ME.

GOOD LORD...

NIGHTWING?

KAFF! KAFF!

HOO!

NIGHTWING!

ANY CHANCE BLOCKBUSTER SURVIVED?

I DON'T SEE HOW.

BUT, WELL... IT MAY TAKE MORE THAN A HOUSE FALLING ON HIM.

I SAW HIM TAKE SIX HOLLOWPOINT BULLETS IN THE CHEST AND SHAKE THEM OFF.

154

155

THESE ARE PROBABLY THE SAME GUYS WHO'VE BEEN JACKING TRUCKS ALL OVER BLÜDHAVEN.

THEY PUT A HALF DOZEN DRIVERS IN THE HOSPITAL ALREADY.

I PUT ALL MY WEIGHT BEHIND MY BEST SHOT.

A GRUNT AND A WHOOSH OF PEPPERONI BREATH TELLS ME I CONNECTED.

SAMSAM CTV-17

WOOOPH!

BUT MY BEST SHOT COSTS ME MY GRIP.

THE ASPHALT REACHES UP FOR ME AS THE TRUCK CORNERS ON STARK AVENUE.

158

TIME TO CHECK INTO THAT TRUST ACCOUNT BRUCE SAID HE HAD SET UP IN MY NAME.

WELL, HI, CLANCY. FUNNY, I'D HAVE EXPECTED TO SEE *YOU* IN A BETTER MOOD.

SURE I'M IN A *FINE* FRAME O' MIND.

REALLY?

I THOUGHT YOU LANDLORDS *LAUGHED* ALL THE WAY TO THE BANK.

OH HO.

WHALER'S BANK OF

HERE T'ROLL ABOUT IN YOUR *FORTUNES*, MR. GRAYSON?

LUCIUS FOX HAS BEEN LOOKING AFTER MONEY LEFT ME BY MY PARENTS.

COULD I GET THE *BALANCE* FROM THIS ACCOUNT?

FDIC INSURED

SURE.

I GUESS THE INTEREST COULD ADD UP AFTER ALL THIS TIME.

THIS IS THE CURRENT BALANCE, MISTER GRAYSON.

FDIC INSURED

IS THERE ANYTHING *ELSE* I CAN DO FOR YOU, MR GRAYSON?

WOO.

160

I SHOULDN'T BE QUITE SO SURPRISED.

LUCIUS FOX IS ONE OF THE MOST BRILLIANT BUSINESSMEN IN THE WORLD.

THE FACILITY ISN'T IN THE *BEST* CONDITION, SIR.

THIS WAS THE LAST NEW CAR DEALER-SHIP TO FAIL IN BLÜDHAVEN.

WILL YOU BE OPENING A BUSINESS OR--

I'D LIKE TO PAY THE FIRST YEAR IN ADVANCE.

WHUH-WHAT?

THAT'LL BE *OKAY*, RIGHT?

UH-- YES! THAT WILL BE-- QUITE OKAY.

LET'S SIGN THE PAPERS THEN.

SHUH-SURE!

NOW THE FUN BEGINS.

ASSEMBLING THE PERFECT VIGILANTE RIDE.

163

LISTEN, THINGS ARE OKAY BETWEEN US RIGHT NOW, BUT YOU DON'T KNOW WHAT IT'S LIKE IN HIS SHADOW.

I DON'T, HUH? HA!

YOU SEEM TO FORGET HOW HE REACTED THE FIRST TIME *I* SHOWED UP IN A CAPE AND BOOTS.

OH, NO I *DON'T*. HE JUST ABOUT HIT THE STALACTITES.

YOU WERE INVITED INTO THE CLUB, DICK.

I JOINED OVER HIS VOCAL DISAPPROVAL.

WE HAD SOME TIMES, RIGHT?

MAYBE WE COULD AGAIN.

168

SOUNDS LIKE A BIG BORE RIFLE.

DID I *WING* THE DEUCED THING, SHAKA?

NO, COLONEL. IT SEEKS COVER BETWEEN THOSE BUILDINGS.

IT'S THESE *CARTRIDGES.* THEY DON'T FLY TRUE.

AND THE FIRING IS DELIBERATE.

HATE TO BREAK UP THE SAFARI, GUYS.

BUT YOU GUYS ARE A *LONG* WAY FROM THE SERENGETI.

I FIGURE THEM FOR A COUPLE OF HEAD-CASES.

UNTIL I SEE THEIR TARGET.

FRANCINE LANGSTROM?

OH.

SORRY TO *STARTLE* YOU BY COMING IN THROUGH THE WINDOW LIKE THIS.

BELIEVE ME, I'M *USED* TO IT.

I'M A FRIEND OF YOUR HUSBAND AND--

AND THE BATMAN. YOU KNEW KIRK IN *BETTER TIMES* AS WELL?

I REMEMBER HIM AS A GREAT MAN, FRANCINE.

FUNNY, IT'S BEEN SO LONG SINCE HE *WAS* A MAN. SOMETIMES I CAN'T PICTURE HIS FACE.

ALL I SEE IS-- IS--

KIRK--

LET ME HELP YOU, FRANCINE.

THAT BOY SAID MR LAW IN 3-B USED TO BE THE TARANTULA.

YOU *LOST* ME, CLANCE.

YOU *WORKIN'* TONIGHT? I THOUGHT WE COULD SEE THAT MOVIE THAT--

SORRY, I'M *BOOKED.*

PROMISED A FAVOR TO A FRIEND. ANOTHER TIME.

Y'GOT A LUCKY FRIEND, MR. GRAYSON.

GOD KNOWS YER THE ONLY NORMAL TENANT IN *THIS* FLATBLOCK.

I HEAR YOU GOT A ROOM TO RENT.

SURE. IT'S AN EFFICIENCY IF Y'DON'T MIND A LITTLE--

OH MY.

JUST ANOTHER HUNTER OUT TO SNARE HIM.

HE DOESN'T KNOW ME.

I'M JUST ANOTHER THREAT.

I HOPE THERE'S AN OPPORTUNITY TO APOLOGIZE LATER.

FEAR'S MAKING HIM EVEN STRONGER.

WOOP!

NOW I KNOW HOW AN OLD SHOE FEELS BEHIND A NEWLYWEDS' CAR.

I'M NOT GOING TO HAVE MUCH UNBRUISED SKIN AREA IF THIS KEEPS UP.

THAT'S IF I DON'T DO A HEADER INTO A LAMP POST FIRST.

197

OR LEVERAGE.

NOT GOING TO BRING HIM DOWN WITHOUT SOME HELP.

I CAN PULL HIM DOWN AND THEN REEL HIM IN.

SCREEEE!

I MAKE IT SOUND SO EASY.

I WASN'T LOOKING FORWARD TO THIS.

KIRK WAS *TAKEN?* KIDNAPPED?

BY *WHOM?*

I DON'T THINK IT WAS A *KIDNAPPING,* MRS. LANGSTROM.

THE MAN WHO TOOK HIM SAID SOME-THING ABOUT MAKING YOUR HUSBAND *FAMOUS.*

FAMOUS? IS HE GOING TO PUT KIRK IN A *FREAK* SHOW?

BLÜD AIR 9E

THIS GUY DOES *NOT* WORK CHEAP.

IT'S PROBABLY SOMETHING MORE *AMBITIOUS* THAN A CIRCUS SIDE-SHOW.

BUT IN THE SAME *SPIRIT.*

IF THEY EXPENDED *THIS* KIND OF ENERGY TO CAPTURE HIM, I'M SURE THEY'RE TAKING GOOD CARE OF HIM.

"GOOD CARE"?

203

LOCKED IN A *CAGE* SOMEWHERE AND FED LIVE *MICE?* I WANT KIRK BACK SO HE CAN BE A *HUMAN* AGAIN. TELL ME YOU'LL *HELP,* NIGHTWING.

WITH EVERYTHING IN MY *POWER,* FRANCINE.

THAT'S AN AWFULLY BIG *PROMISE* I MADE.

IT'S BEEN AN HOUR SINCE I WOKE UP ON THAT ROOFTOP AFTER DEATHSTROKE'S "MERCY" DART WORE OFF.

AND I WAS OUT FOR *THREE* HOURS BEFORE THAT.

THEY COULD BE *ANYWHERE* IN THE WORLD BY NOW.

AND IF I *FIND* THEM, I HAVE TO GO UP AGAINST THE TOUGHEST MERCENARY IN THE WORLD.

WELL, IF BEING A HERO WAS *EASY* THEN I GUESS *EVERY-ONE* WOULD DO IT.

SEE IF BARBARA'S AWAKE AND ON LINE.

THE TWO OF US SHOULD BE ABLE TO COME UP WITH AN EDUCATED GUESS OR TWO.

POOM! POOM!

POOM!

SOUNDS LIKE SOMEONE TRAINING ELEPHANTS UPSTAIRS.

THERE'S SOMETHING GOING ON IN THE APARTMENT ABOVE ME, CLANCY.

I JUST RENTED IT OUT, DICK.

IN FACT, HERE'S YOUR NEW NEIGHBOR, MR--

ULP.

YOU WANT ME TO FIND OUT WHERE DEATHSTROKE TOOK A HUMAN BAT.

FOR THE AMOUNT OF MONEY HE USUALLY CHARGES, SLADE WILSON PROBABLY HAS *ANY* MEANS OF TRANSPORTATION AT HIS DISPOSAL.

AND HE'S GOT AN EIGHT-HOUR HEAD START.

THAT'S ABOUT THE *SIZE OF IT,* BABS.

WHY CAN'T YOU GUYS EVER CALL WITH AN *EASY* ONE?

A RECIPE FOR CARROT CAKE. WHETHER OR NOT SEINFELD'S A *RERUN* TONIGHT.

CARROT CAKE SOUNDS BETTER THAN A SOGGY BOWL OF CORN FLAKES.

I KINDA LIKE 'EM SOGGY.

EW. AND I WAS *JUST* ABOUT TO PROPOSE.

COOL YOUR *PIPES,* GRAYSON.

WE'LL LOOK INTO MY CRYSTAL BALL AND SEE WHAT WE SHALL SEE.

PREPARE FOR OPTION PARALYSIS.

MAN-BAT POPS UP ON THE WEB JUST BEHIND SASQUATCH AND THE SWAMP THING.

LOTS OF ENTRIES?

SCREENS FULL. MOST OF THE SIGHTINGS ARE BOGUS.

DEATHSTROKE SAID THAT LANGSTROM WOULD BE FAMOUS.

ANYTHING ELSE?

I BLACKED OUT AFTER THAT.

AN ENTERTAINMENT ANGLE THEN.

WE'LL PARALLEL-SEARCH UNDER "FREAKS", "ODDITIES" AND "PARANORMAL".

WILL THIS TAKE LONG?

TAKE A NAP, DICK. I'LL BUZZ YOU WHEN I FIND SOMETHING.

YOU'RE A PRINCESS, BABS.

HUH. GOOD NIGHT, FORMER BOY WONDER.

and while the Axis Powers were rolling over half the world, a battle of a different sort was going on in the streets and alleys of America. A more insidious war waged by gangsters, profiteers and saboteurs.

It took a special breed of crimefighter to stem this tide of treason. It took a man willing to work outside the law and its binding conventions.

"THE KIND OF MAN WHO WAS WILLING TO SUFFER SCORN RATHER THAN INJUSTICE.

FAD'S CRIB
STAY OUT OR DIE

"A MAN WHO COULD SEPARATE THE WHEAT FROM THE CHUA-CHAFF?

"--AND WEED OUT THE CRIMINAL PARASITES OF OUR SOCIETY.

WUUP? WUUP?
WUUP!

WHUZZ?

MOONLIGHT'S IN THE CANYON, BUCKAROO.

YOU FOUND SOMETHING ON THE *NET*, BABS?

ON CHANNEL *FIVE!* TURN IT ON!

THEY'VE BEEN *PROMOING* THIS ALL DAY.

IT'S ONE OF THOSE STUPID *INFOTAINMENT* SHOWS.

IT'S A LEAD.

-- *KIND OF SHOW-MANSHIP* YOU'D EXPECT FROM RUDOLF MULDOON. WE JOIN HIM LIVE ON ONE OF HIS MANY CARGO SHIPS --

KEEP WATCHING.

CAN YOU GIVE US A HINT OF WHAT THIS IS ABOUT, RUDOLF?

JUST A HINT, MYRA. I'VE BEEN ON SAFARI AND BROUGHT BACK THE STRANGEST CREATURE MAN HAS EVER SEEN.

HAVE YOU BEEN TO AFRICA?

NO, MYRA. I'VE BEEN TO THE URBAN JUNGLE.

BINGO?

DEFINITELY BINGO.

A FEW KEYSTROKES AND BABS HAD THE PROBABLE LOCATION OF MULDOON'S SHIP.

MY BOAT'S FAST BUT I STILL HAD TO PUSH HER TO THE LIMIT TO CATCH UP.

SET HER TO MATCH SPEED AND FOLLOW ME.

WORRY LATER ABOUT HOW I'M GONNA GET KIRK ABOARD.